Long *i*: *i*_e

Nice, Nice

by Liza Charleswo

ISBN: 978-1-338-84441-2

Art Director: Tannaz Fassihi; Designer: Cynthia Ng; Illustrated by Michael Robertson

3 4 5 6 68 26 25 24

Printed in Jiaxing, China. First printing, June 2022.

It is Ike.
It is Mike.
Ike and Mike are
nice, nice mice!

Ike and Mike like
to fly a big kite.

Ike and Mike like
to take a big hike.

Ike and Mike like
to ride a mile
on a big bike.

Ride, ride!
Ike and Mike see Bee.

Ride, ride!
Ike and Mike see Rat.

Ride, ride!
Ike and Mike see Bat.

Ride, ride!
Ike and Mike see ice cream.

Ike and Mike get
five big lime cones.
1, 2, 3, 4, 5.

Ride, ride!
Ride, ride!
Ride, ride!

Ike and Mike take a cone
to Bee, Rat, and Bat.

It is time to dine on lime ice cream...

with nice, nice mice.
Life is fine!

Read & Review

Invite your learner to point to each long-*i* word and read it aloud.

mile
kite
nice
bike
Ike
dine
life
mice
ride
like
five
time

Fun Fill-Ins

Read the sentences aloud, inviting your learner to complete them using the long-*i* words in the box.

mice fine kite Mike bike

1. The mice in this story are Ike and ______.
2. Ike and Mike are nice, nice ______.
3. Ike and Mike fly a big ______.
4. Ike and Mike ride a big ______.
5. The last sentence of the story is: Life is ______!